101 Curling Excuses

101 Curling Excuses

Created by David Feldstein   Cartoons by Frank McCourt

101 Publishing

First published in the USA and Canada in 2011 by 101 Publishing

Printed in the USA

ISBN 978-0-9869276-0-7

The authors would like to acknowledge that many of Frank McCourt's cartoons in this book first appeared in the Ontario Curling Report.

Introduction

It all started one cold, dark, wintry night in the northern reaches of Canada. Indoors on a sheet of ice 146 feet long and 14 feet wide were 16 granite rocks and two teams of four players each. The sport of the great white north ... CURLING ..... David and Frank met on the curling ice in Canada. Yup, that was the birthplace of 101 Excuses. Here's how it started.

Curling is a sport that requires extraordinary teamwork and skill in order to be played well. Being the ultimate team sport, it's also a very social game. One of the first things you notice when you take up curling is that no matter what happens on the ice, it's not your fault. It could be the broom's fault, the rock, the ice, whatever, but "excuses" are flying around all over the place.

Suddenly it came to them. Someone needed to assemble these excuses in order to arm curlers, both new and experienced, with the tools they need to survive the curling season. David and Frank got to work. Of course, the two of them had plenty of excuses as to why they couldn't do the book, but in the end they realized it was their mission. The rest, my friends, is history.

101 CURLING EXCUSES #57

" THE **CURLING GODS** WERE **AGAINST US.**"

- ☐ JOIN A CURLING CLUB.
- ☐ BECOME A CLUB LEAD.
- ☐ BECOME A CLUB SECOND.
- ☐ BECOME A CLUB THIRD.
- ☐ BECOME A CLUB SKIP.
- ☐ BECOME A COMPETITIVE LEAD.
- ☐ BECOME A COMPETITIVE SECOND.
- ☐ BECOME A COMPETITIVE THIRD.
- ☐ BECOME A COMPETITIVE SKIP.
- ☐ WIN A GAME.
- ☐ WIN A SPIEL.
- ☐ WIN A MIXED GAME.
- ☐ WIN A GAME WITH YOUR SPOUSE.
- ☐ WIN A GAME WITH YOUR SON/DAUGHTER.
- ☐ WIN THE LAST GAME OF THE YEAR.
- ☐ WIN MORE GAMES THAN YOU LOST IN A SEASON.
- ☐ WIN A CLUB CHAMPIONSHIP.
- ☐ CURL IN A PLAYOFF GAME.
- ☐ CURL IN A PROVINCIAL.
- ☐ CURL IN A NATIONAL.
- ☐ CURL IN A WORLDS.
- ☐ CURL ON TV.
- ☐ WIN A COMPETITIVE SPIEL.
- ☐ WIN A ZONE.
- ☐ WIN A REGION.

The Authors

David Feldstein was born in the Bronx in 1953, attended the Julliard School of Music in Manhattan and graduated from Berklee College of Music in Boston. Well known in the recording industry, he spent his career as a composer, writing music for television shows and commercials. He is known in the music industry for such works as the Siskel and Ebert theme, USA Today on TV, music for ABC's 20/20 and hundreds of commercial scores. Upon retiring from the music business he took up curling and immediately fell in love with the game. David quickly began to notice all the excuses flying around the curling rink. As time went on he realized he just had to write 101 Curling Excuses. Once he met Frank, the die was cast.

Frank McCourt was born in Toronto in 1954. He served for 33 years as a Captain on the Toronto Fire Service. A self-taught cartoonist, Frank fell in love with the game of curling. Frank curled with World Champions Ed Werenich and Neil Harrison, fellow fire fighters who introduced him to the Ontario Curling Report, the paper where he has drawn editorials and Boomer (his cartoon strip) for over 27 years. Frank has also illustrated curling books such as Curling for Dummies, Idiots Guide to Curling, Little Rocks, Coaches Manuals, as well as curling calendars and greeting cards. Frank enjoys the nickname given to him by The Sports Network, "Canada's Curling Cartoonist ".

Printed in Great Britain
by Amazon.co.uk, Ltd.,
Marston Gate.